Colors

Written by Helen Depree
Illustrated by Marina McAllan

Blow up a green balloon.
Blow up a blue balloon.
Blow up a yellow balloon.
Blow up a red balloon.
Blow up a purple balloon.
This is a bunch of balloons
for a birthday party.

3

Cut up a yellow banana.
Cut up an orange papaya.
Cut up some green kiwifruit.
Cut up some red plums.
Cut up some purple grapes.
This is some fruit salad
for lunch.

Mix in some green lettuce.
Mix in a red tomato.
Mix in an orange carrot.
Mix in some yellow egg yolk.
Mix in some purple cabbage.
This is a vegetable salad
for dinner.

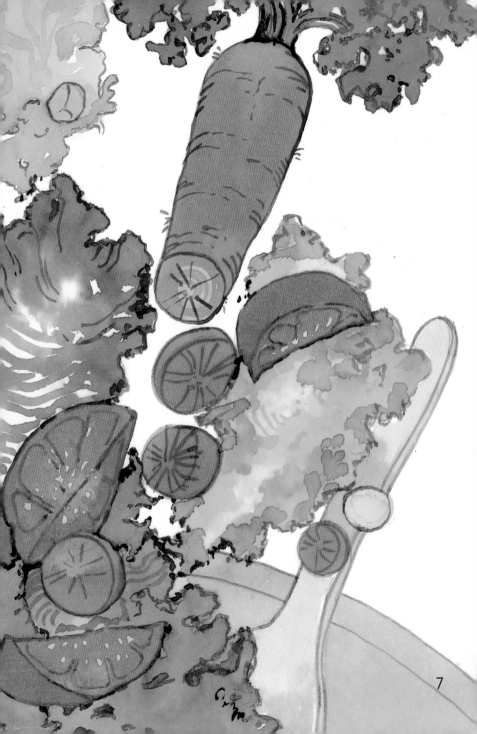

Drop in a blue sweater.
Drop in a red skirt.
Drop in a yellow shirt.
Drop in some green socks.
Drop in some purple pants.
This is a load of clothes
for the washing machine.

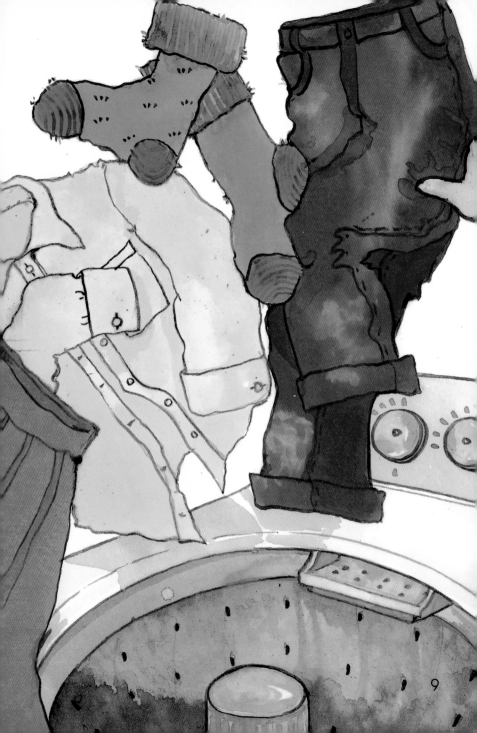

Pick a red flower.
Pick a yellow flower.
Pick a blue flower.
Pick a purple flower.
Pick an orange flower.
This is a bunch of flowers
for Grandma.

10

Put in a purple car.
Put in a red train.
Put in a yellow teddy bear.
Put in a green frog.
Put in a blue block.
This is a basket of toys
to play with.